N. Patron

Too Hot To Hoot

Too Hot To Hoot

THE PALINDROME PUZZLE BOOK

Raymond Stuart

Pictures by
Pamela Baldwin Ford

David McKay Company, Inc.
New York

Library of Congress Cataloging in Publication Data

Stuart, Raymond.
Too hot to hoot.

SUMMARY: A picture puzzle book consisting of jumbled
captions which, when the letters are rearranged, spell
out a palindrome.
1. Picture puzzles—Juvenile literature.
2. Palindromes. [1. Picture puzzles. 2. Palindromes]
I. Baldwin-Ford, Pamela. II. Title.
GV1507.P47S85   793.7′3   77-5238
ISBN 0-679-20404-0

10 9 8 7 6 5 4 3 2 1

For
my daughter,
Andrea, who first introduced me to
palindromes

OTO OTH OT OTOH

The word *pop* is a palindrome. It reads the same backward as it does forward. The title of this book, *Too Hot To Hoot,* is a palindrome sentence. It too reads the same backward as it does forward.

The object of each of the puzzles in the following pages is to find the right caption, in the form of a palindrome, for each picture.

For example, suppose you wanted to find the caption for the picture of the owl on the facing page. Your first step would be to copy the letters OTO OTH OT OTOH beneath the picture on a separate piece of paper. Then you would look at the picture for the clue to the caption. If you re-arranged the scrambled letters into a palindrome sentence containing four words, you would discover that the picture's caption is TOO HOT TO HOOT.

Once you have solved all the puzzles in the book, you can share them with others *if* you make sure not to write in the book itself. Remember to get a pencil and some paper before you begin to solve the puzzles.

1. MALLA LALM *(two words)*

2. "WASP WASP."   *(two words)*

3. POT TOPS   *(two words)*

4. SEBSOS OBS. *(two words)*

5. ALP SSEE ALP. *(three words)*

6. ITP A TIP.   *(three words)*

7. TSAR ESES TASR.   *(three words)*

8. "AMADM, M'I MAAD." *(three words)*

9. PEST NO ON PEST. *(four words)*

10. "LUPL PU FI I LUPL PU." *(six words)*

11. "SIRE OT ETOV, ISR." *(four words)*

12.   A NAM, A NALP, A LANCA, ANAMPA

(seven words)

13. SAW TI A TAC I ASW? *(six words)*

14. ESINDN NAD NADE DINSEN.
(four words)

15. ROPO NAD SI NI A PROOD.
(six words)

16. "VEA, NAC I BAST BAST NI A VACE?"
    (eight words)

17. "LEFE OT EM, OTERME FLE."

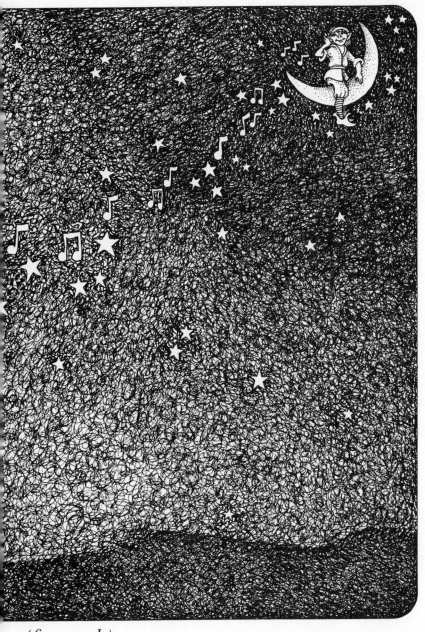

(five words)

Answers

You will be able to read the answers to each puzzle by holding this page in front of a mirror.

1. Llama mall
2. "Swap paws."
3. Top spot
4. Bosses sob.
5. Pal sees lap.
6. Tip a pit.
7. Star sees rats.
8. "Madam, I'm Adam."
9. Step on no pets.
10. "Pull up if I pull up."
11. "Rise to vote, sir."
12. A man, a plan, a canal, Panama
13. Was it a cat I saw?
14. Dennis and Edna sinned.
15. Poor Dan is in a droop.
16. "Eva, can I stab bats in a cave?"
17. "Flee to me, remote elf."